DREAMLAND
KID'S
4th Activity Book

Age 6+
English

Compiled by :
Shweta Shilpa

DREAMLAND PUBLICATIONS

J-128, Kirti Nagar, New Delhi-110 015, India
Tel. : +91-11- 2510 6050, 2543 5657
E-mail : dreamland@dreamlandpublications.com
Shop online at www.dreamlandpublications.com
Follow us on www.instagram.com/dreamland.publications

Published in 2021 by

DREAMLAND PUBLICATIONS

J-128, Kirti Nagar, New Delhi - 110 015, India
Tel. : +91-11-2510 6050, 2543 5657
E-mail : dreamland@dreamlandpublications.com
www.dreamlandpublications.com

ISBN 978-81-8451-651-7

Printed in India

PREFACE

This 4th Activity Book is indeed a treasure house of fun filled moments. Every page of this book is full of entertaining assignments for children. This book on **"English"** will enhance the child in grasping and understanding about the basic concepts of the English language.

Children will find the book interesting by involving themselves in solving mazes, adding colour to the drawings, matching the pairs, etc., and will have fun with dots and puzzles. At times, they may have to complete half-finished sketches or spot differences between pictures that almost look alike, thereby giving them a chance to think cohesively.

An attempt has been made not only to entertain but also stimulate the child's thinking, reasoning and creativity.

This book aims at providing children with a way to relax after a strenuous day of vigorous outdoor activity.

—Publisher

Vowels and Consonants

Read the letters and write ◇V for vowels
and ◇C for consonants

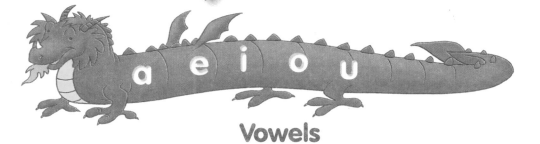

Vowels

Consonants

g ◇   q ◇   b ◇   P ◇

a ◇   t ◇   e ◇   m ◇

u ◇   i ◇   f ◇   J ◇

W ◇   j ◇   s ◇

Find 'ar' words in the puzzle. Colour each
book when you find it.

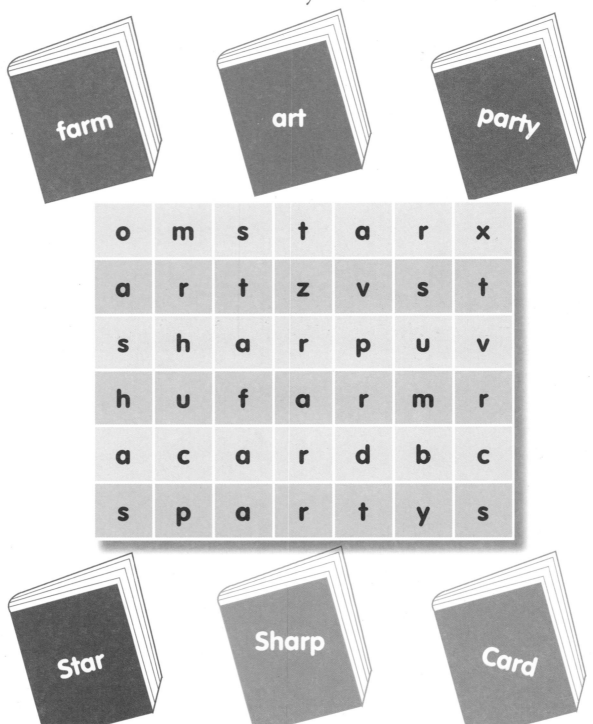

farm

art

party

o	m	s	t	a	r	x
a	r	t	z	v	s	t
s	h	a	r	p	u	v
h	u	f	a	r	m	r
a	c	a	r	d	b	c
s	p	a	r	t	y	s

Star

Sharp

Card

Mischievious Vowels

Some of the vowels are hidden in the sentences given below. Read the sentences and circle the vowels. One is done for you.

THE BAG IS ON THE RACK

MY RED PURSE IS BIG

THE BABY IS PLAYING WITH BLOCKS

HE IS SLEEPING IN THE BED

MUMMY IS COOKING IN THE KITCHEN

A CAP IS ON THE TABLE

Look at the first picture in each row. Tick the other picture in the same row that start in the same way.

Sp

(spoon) (spider) (star)

Sn

(snake) (cup) (snail)

Cl

(clown) (clock) (crown)

Gr

(grass) (grapes) (fish)

Arrange letters in a sequence to make a word. The first one is done for you.

Tin

_____

_____

_____

_____

_____

_____

_____

_____

_____

Join the words written in flowers and leaves to make the correct compound word and write in the space provided.

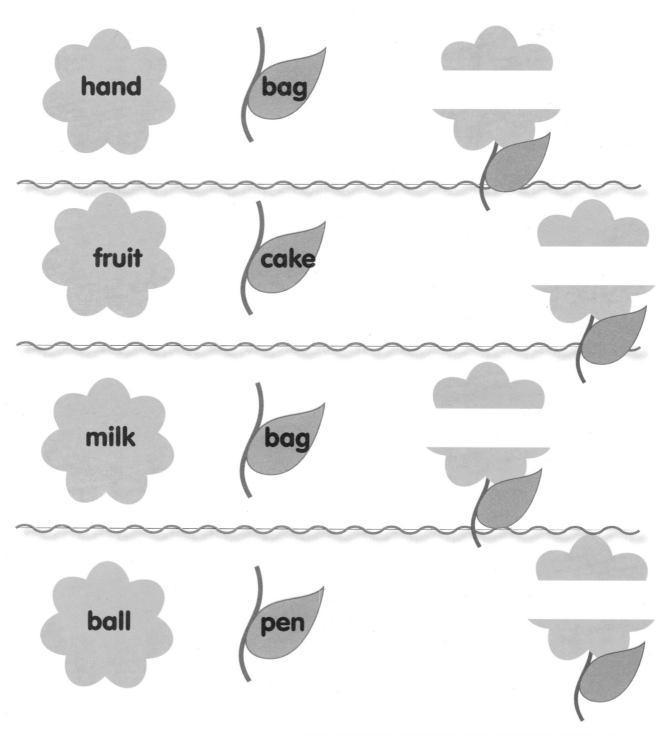

Kass likes things that end with the letters as in his name. What are they?
Colour the pictures.

Word Fun

Find the matching words of those given below from the help box.

bear,   pear,   fair,   mail,   hear

bare	
hare	
pair	
male	
fare	

The bees are carrying hidden words. Find them and write in the space provided. One is done for you.

us
_____   _____

_____   _____   _____

_____   _____   _____

_____   _____

Say these double sounds. Choose the right one to finish each word. Write in the space provided.

ss   ng   ch   ck   sh

du __ __

gra __ __

fi __ __

wat __ __

spri __ __

Read the words in each scarf and colour the odd one out.

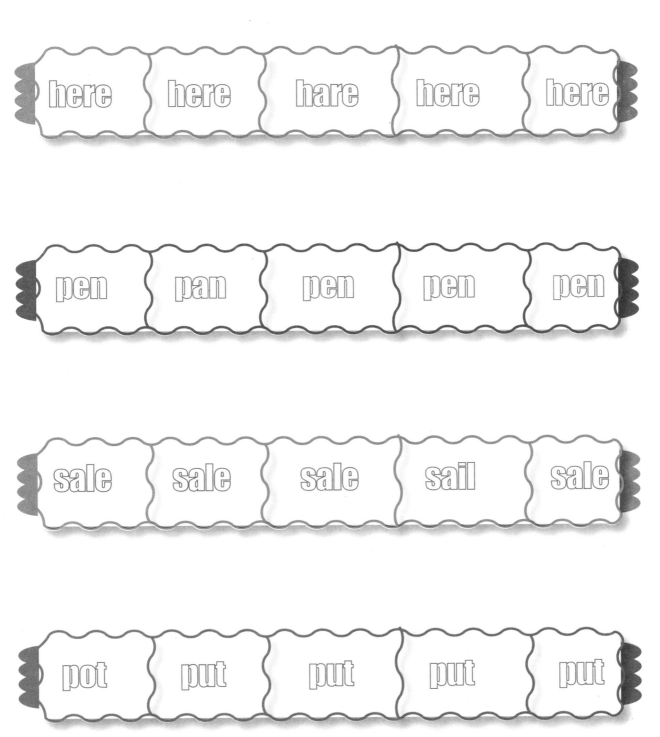

here · here · hare · here · here

pen · pan · pen · pen · pen

sale · sale · sale · sail · sale

pot · put · put · put · put

Count the letters in each cloud. Write each word in the correct rocket.

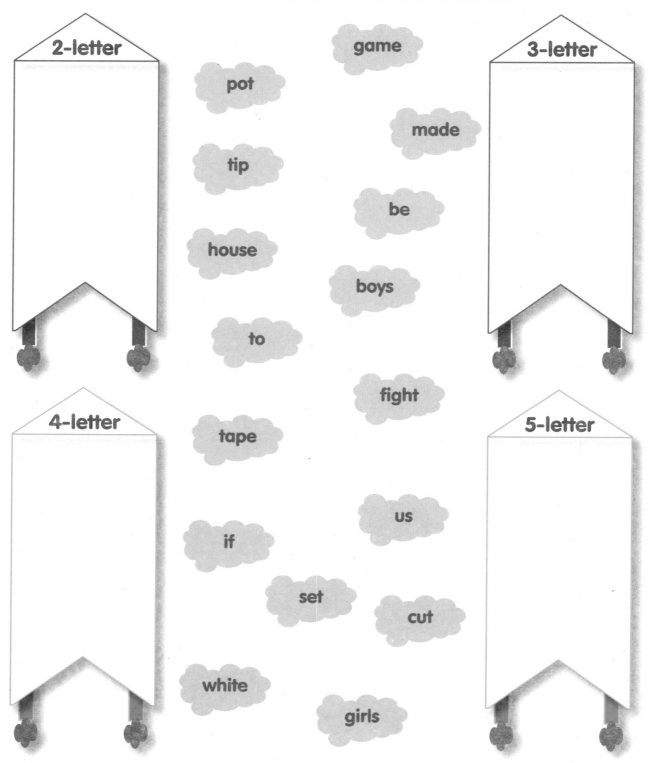

Help Sim choose the right double sounds to start each word and write in the space provided.

Please help

_ _ _ apes

_ _ _ ee

_ _ _ oon

_ _ _ ail

sn

tr

sp

gr

Initial and final sounds
Hey! C'mon let's complete the words by filling in the first and the last sound.

__ u __

__ u __

__ rai __

__ ai __

__ ir __

Game Time

Help Roxy in scoring full marks by ticking the correct spellings of the words given

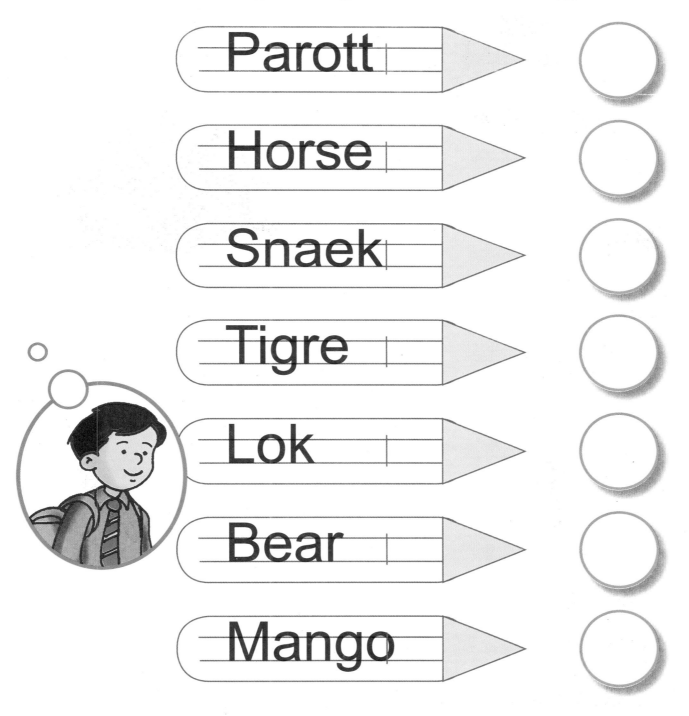

Parott

Horse

Snaek

Tigre

Lok

Bear

Mango

Read these sentences. Encircle the capital letters and full stop in each sentence.

We get milk from cows.

This is a hut.

Ronn likes oranges.

I have a red balloon.

A giraffe is eating leaves.

Unscramble the letters

Unscramble the jumbled letters to find the naming words.

The sentences given below are all muddled. Write them in the correct order.

1. Is Mac fat

_____

2. Is a doctor He

_____

3. Is morning It

_____

4. A jug this is

_____

Choose the words from the box and place them in the correct curtain.

kite   owl   egg   rat   bell

astronaut   umbrella   flower   cat

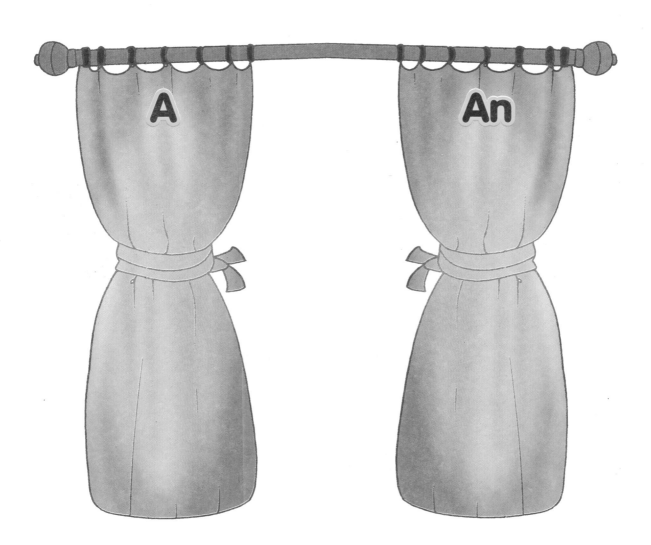

A

An

One-Many

Add 'S' to make these words mean more than one and write in the space provided. One is done for you.

 **Cat + S =**

Cats

 **Key + S =**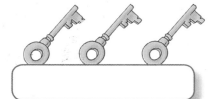

 **Bag + S =**

 **Fan + S =**

 **bell + S =**

Joining is Fun
Join the words with the pictures. One is done for you.

gate

frog

apple

door

axe

well

snake

ring

Muddled Up Words

Unscramble the letters in the grid to discover a word. As a clue, read the picture given below to find the answer.

1.

M	A
T	E

 = _____

2.

O	H
M	E

= _____

3.

R	A
I	H

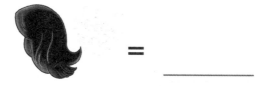 = _____

4.

I	L
K	M

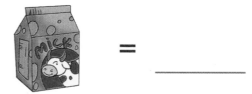 = _____

5.

T	E
E	R

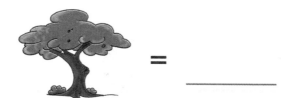 = _____

6.

L	A
B	L

 = _____

Help Mike to use 'This' or 'That' in the following sentences.

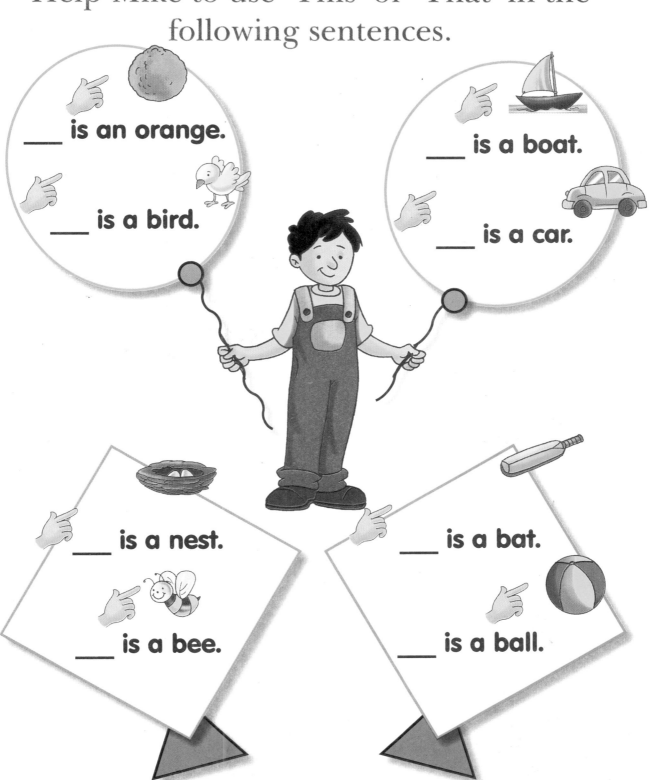

___ is an orange.

___ is a bird.

___ is a boat.

___ is a car.

___ is a nest.

___ is a bee.

___ is a bat.

___ is a ball.

Fill in the blanks with the words written in the rocket.

1. A glass is ____ the table.

2. A flower is ____ the pot.

2 3 4

3. Three is ____ two and four.

4. A leaf is ____ the umbrella.

Break the codes given below to find the secret words.

	1	2	3	4	5
A	R	S	K	H	B
B	D	E	U	G	L
C	X	J	W	C	N
D	Y	I	O	Q	F
E	M	V	T	P	A

C 2   B 3   E 1   E 4

A 1   B 3   C 5

A 4   D 3   E 4

B 2   E 5   E 3

Help Tim in rearranging the words to form correct sentences.

is raining It

_____

a is flower This

_____

bag My heavy is

_____

Stars shining are

_____

Write the first letter of each object in the blanks to find the name of an animal.

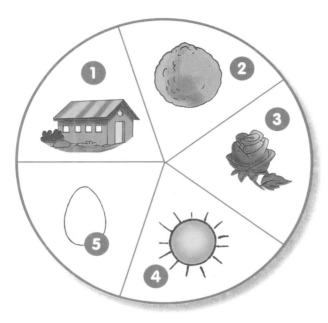

_____ _____ _____ _____ _____

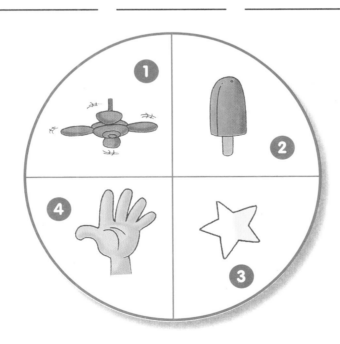

_____ _____ _____ _____

Make sentences using the words in the clouds

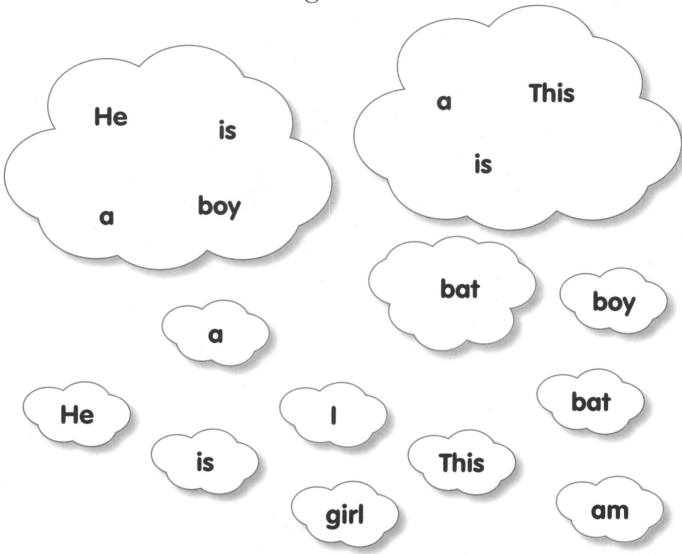

Example : I am a girl.

1. _____

2. _____

Choose the right word to complete each sentence.

Hot   Cold

Tea is _____

Heavey   Light

Feather is _____

Soft   Hard

A pillow is _____

The robot gives the opposite of the word that goes in. Write the opposite that comes out.

In

Out

Big

Open

Day

More

Out · Night
Small
Close · Less

Game on vowel.
Tickle your mind and make 4 more words
usings vowel 'i' . One is done for you.

Example p i n

1. _____

2. _____

Clues

3. _____

4. _____

Brain Teaser.
Solve the puzzle and find the hidden words.

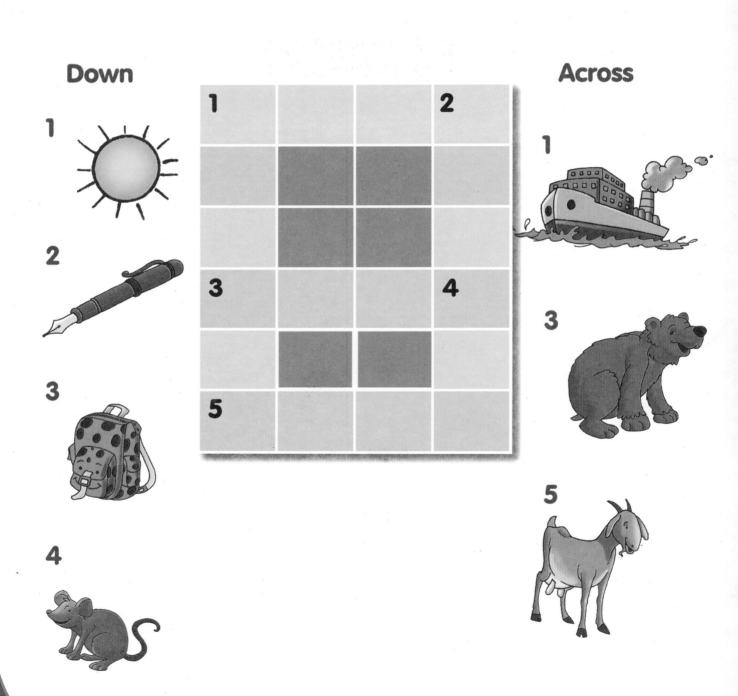

Down

1
2
3
4

Across

1
3
5

Word Hunt.

Search the words in the grid by looking at the pictures given.

	M	X	Z				
	Y	B	M	L			
	H	A	U	T			
X	A	G	R	S			
N	T	B	R	X	Y		
F	P	H	D	O	C	B	L
I	Q	G	J	S	U	N	Q
C	S	H	I	P	E	P	N	M	N
D	H	U	T	S	V	I	W	K	J
E	A	Y	T	Z	B	E	A	R	O	X	P

Rhyme Time.

I am sure you must be fond of rhymes.
So, let's read the rhyme given below and
underline the rhyming words in it.

Churmura Churmura Churmura
Yeh Yeh Churmura
My papa gave me yen
To buy one pen
But I want Churmura

My papa gave me cent
To buy one tent
But I want churmura

My papa gave me dollar
To buy one collar
But I want churmura

My papa gave me pound
To listen to a sound
But I want churmura.

Join the blends in the snakes to form a new word. Use the pictures' clues and write the word in the eggs.

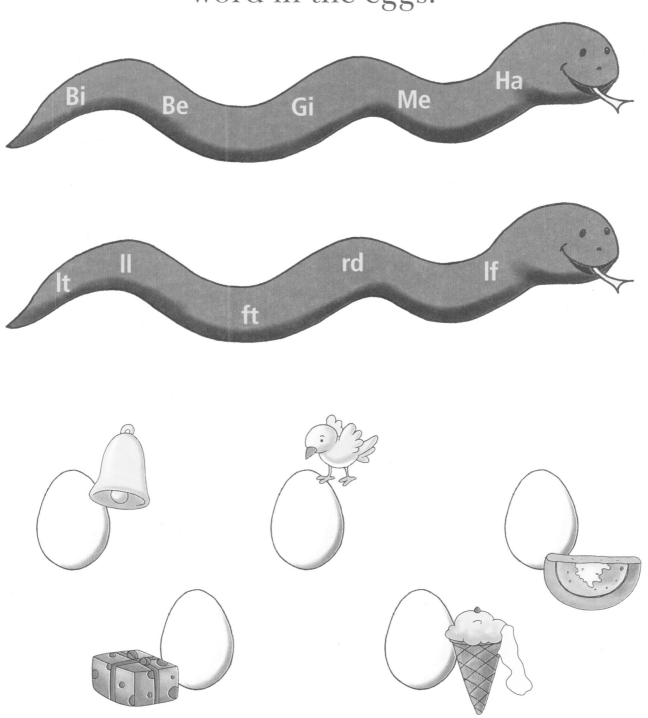

Read the sentences and draw the pictures.

Draw a duck on the river

Draw a house under the tree

Draw a bird between two clouds

Draw moon above the stars

Use has / have in the sentences given below.

Suzie _____ a book.

Tim and Tom _____ a kite.

She _____ a ballon.

Do you _____ my bottle?

I _____ a flower.

Read and tick (✓) the correct answer.

I am Katty, the cat

Who is Katty?

a. Katty is a bird ☐

b. Katty is a cat ☐

I sit on the mat

Where does Katty sit?

a. Katty sits on the mat ☐

b. Katty sits on the couch ☐

I like to drink milk

What does Katty like to drink?

a. Katty does not like to drink milk ☐

b. Katty likes to drink milk ☐

Write words you can make from the letters in the word 'aeroplane'. One is done for you.

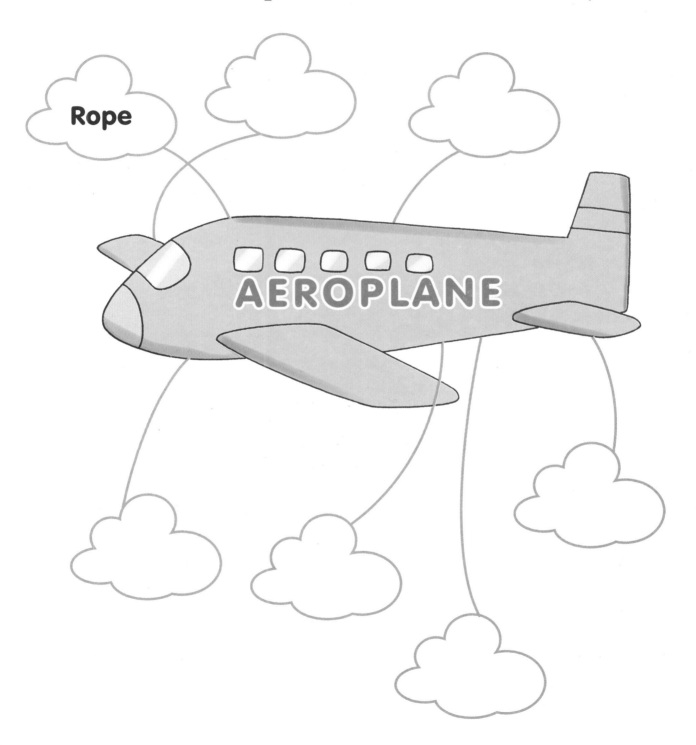

Rope

AEROPLANE

Join the sounds in the bubbles to the correct pictures.

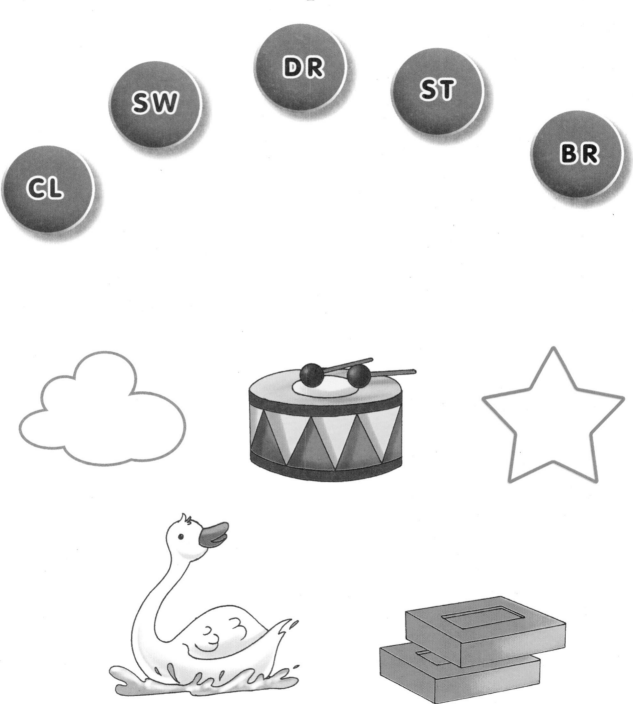

Say the name of each thing. Encircle the
sound in the middle of each name.

There are many words in the bucket.
Write only the naming words
in the clothes hanged.

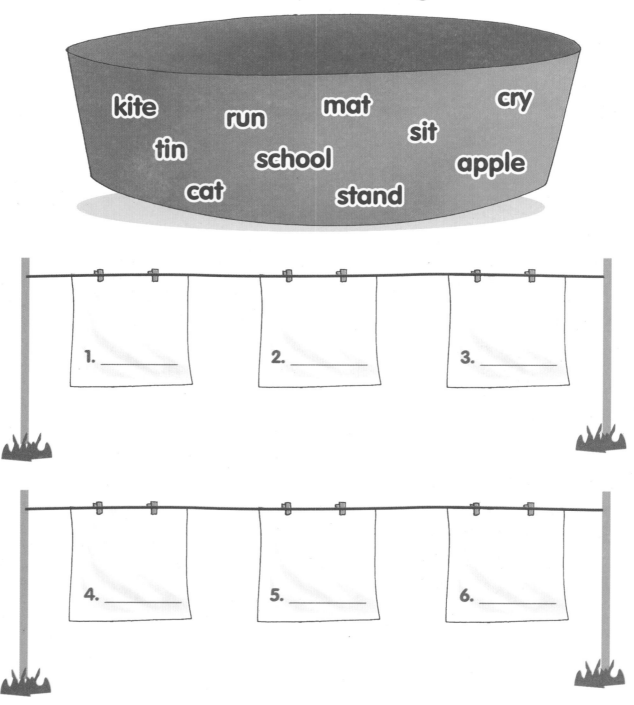

kite   run   mat   cry   sit
tin   school   apple   cat   stand

1. _____

2. _____

3. _____

4. _____

5. _____

6. _____

Tick (✓) the set of words that are sentences and put a cross (✗) by the set of words that are not sentences. One is done for you.

Two ships are sailing in water. ✓

Plants in water. ☐

Water is blue. ☐

There are three fish. ☐

Cold water. ☐

Green plants. ☐

Let's build our vocabulary.
Read the words in the box, then write each
one in the right book, one is done for you.

bicycle, sunny, road, ship, windy, cold, hot air balloon, rainy

FOODS

bread

macaroni

pizza

burger

WEATHER

TRANSPORT

Cool baby!
Find the 'oo' words in the puzzle given below,
one is done for you.

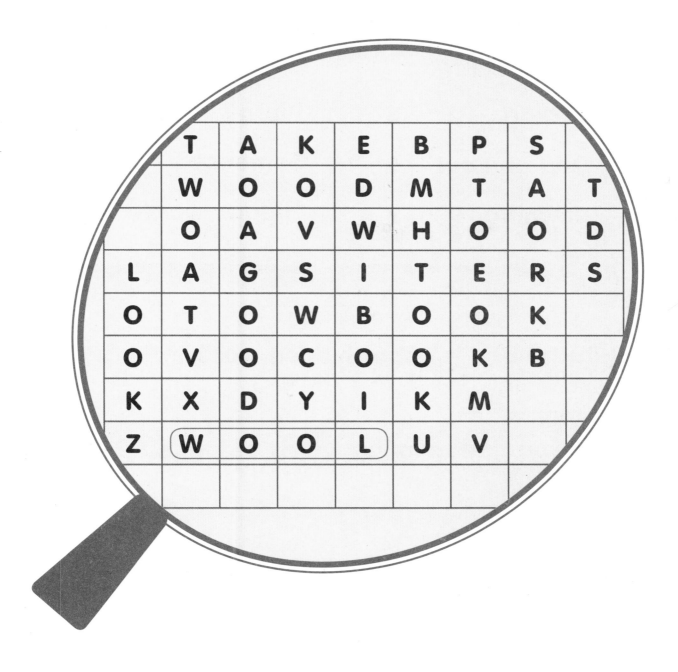

T	A	K	E	B	P	S	
W	O	O	D	M	T	A	T
O	A	V	W	H	O	O	D
L	A	G	S	I	T	E	R	S
O	T	O	W	B	O	O	K
O	V	O	C	O	O	K	B
K	X	D	Y	I	K	M	
Z	W	O	O	L	U	V	

Instructions: Find the words in horizontal & vertical directions.

Read the contents of the book given below and answer the following question.

Contents		Contents	
Sorting	3	Plurals	9
Odd one out	5	Sentences	12
Rhyming	7	Hidden words	17

Which page is about hidden words?

_____

Can you find rhyming words on page 7 ?

(Yes / No)_____

Are the contents in alphabetical order?

(Yes / No)_____

Read the words on the television screen below and write another word that starts with each of these letter blends.

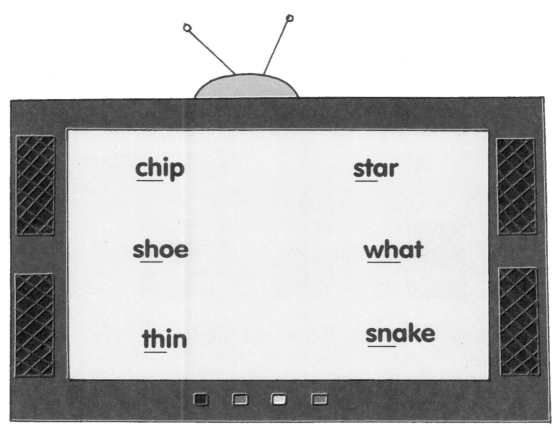

chip   star

shoe   what

thin   snake

Ch _____   St _____

Sh _____   Wh _____

Th _____   Sn _____

Some children did a survey of their favourite pet, see the graph and answer the following questions.

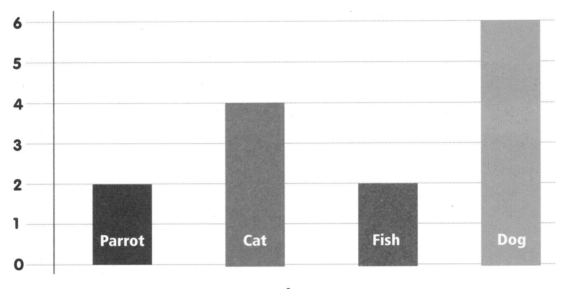

Popular pet

Which is the most popular pet?

_____

How many children chose cat?

_____

Name two pets that are equally popular.

_____

See the picture and fill in the blanks with the words given in the help box.

stops,   stands,   eats,   plays,   gives

The dog _____ on the mat.

The car _____ at the red light.

Tom _____ with the ball.

Kim _____ a slice of cake.

John _____ a gift to Jane.

Help Jenny to use this telephone directory to answer the question given below.

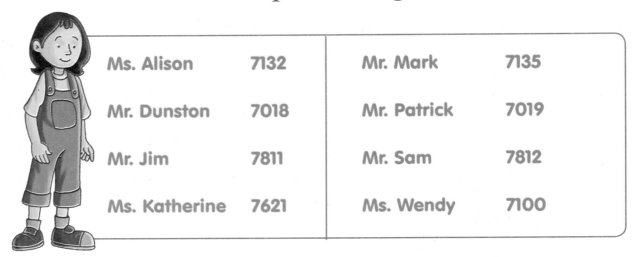

Ms. Alison	7132	Mr. Mark	7135
Mr. Dunston	7018	Mr. Patrick	7019
Mr. Jim	7811	Mr. Sam	7812
Ms. Katherine	7621	Ms. Wendy	7100

What is Ms. Alison's number?

_____

What is Mr. Mark's number?

_____

What is Mr. Sam's number?

_____

Whose number is 7100 ?

_____

Whose number is 7811?

_____

Look at the names and then write them in the register in alphabetical order.

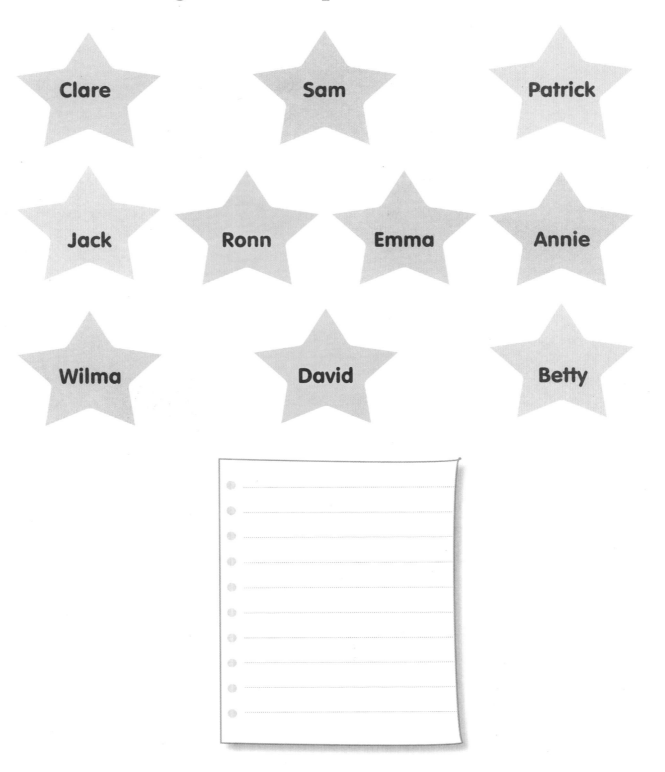

Clare

Sam

Patrick

Jack

Ronn

Emma

Annie

Wilma

David

Betty

Use 'is', 'are' in the following sentences.

This _____ a house.

 We _____ friends.

He _____ a teacher.

 You _____ cute.

The words on the page have incorrect spellings. See the picture and write the correct spellings.

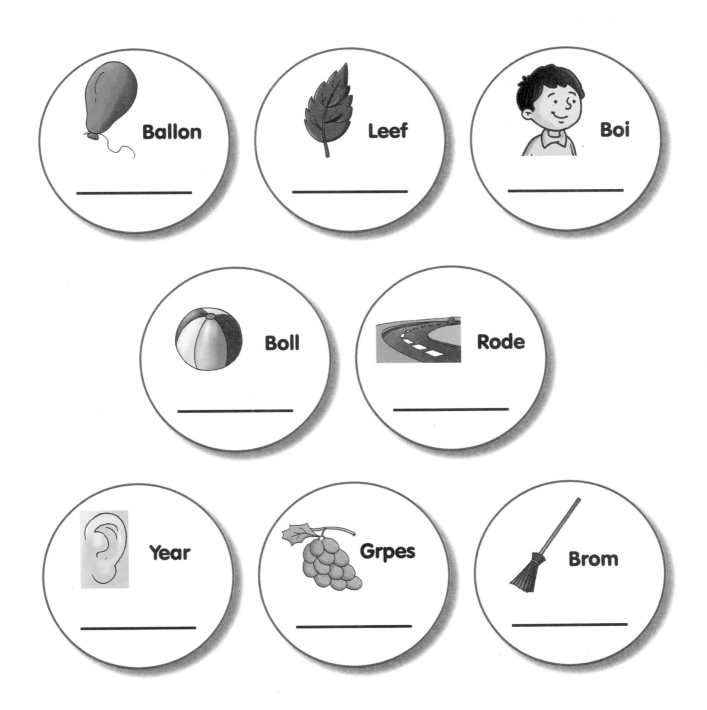

Ballon

_____

Leef

_____

Boi

_____

Boll

_____

Rode

_____

Year

_____

Grpes

_____

Brom

_____

Read the birthday chart and answer the questions given below.

JANUARY	FEBRUARY	MARCH	APRIL
Tom	Steve	Tim	Peter
MAY	JUNE	JULY	AUGUST
Paul	Marry, Jane	Mark, Jim, Suzie	Dick
SEPTEMBER	OCTOBER	NOVEMBER	DECEMBER
Sally	Kelly	Patrick	

1. **When is Sally's birthday?**

   _____

2. **When is Steve's birthday?**

   _____

3. **Which month has no birthday?**

   _____

4. **Whose birthday is in the month of April?**

   _____

5. **Which months have the most birthdays?**

   _____

Use 'these' or 'those' in the following sentences.

_____ are pencils.

_____ are flowers.

_____ are birds.

_____ are grapes.

_____ are sweets.

Help Jane to make new words.

1. Change the 'f' in fish to 'd'   _____

2. Change the 't' in toy to 'b'   _____

3. Change the 'b' in bun to 'f'   _____

4. Change the 'f' in fire to 'w'   _____

5. Change the 'b' in bark to 'sp'   _____

Peter, Dick and Tom are going for a picnic. They have made a list of what they will carry in their lunch box. Read the list and answer the questions.

PETER

Apples

Chocolate

Drink

TOM

Banana

Pizza

Grilled sandwich

DICK

Cheese roll

Pineapple cake

Yoghurt

1. Who has yoghurt ? _____

2. Who has apples ? _____

3. Who has grilled sandwich ? _____

Read the instructions and then draw on the pictures.

1. Draw Daniel's eyes and nose.
2. Colour Emma's skirt in green.
3. Draw a smile on Ronn's face.
4. Draw a pocket on Ronn's T-shirt.
5. Draw a bow-tie on Emma's shirt.

| Daniel | Emma | Ronn |

See the picture and describe it in five sentences.

Cross out the word that does not belong in each row.

Colours

red	pink	bell	blue

Shapes

oval	square	size	circle

Vehicles

bus	van	nib	car

Flowers

orchid	rose	leaf	lotus

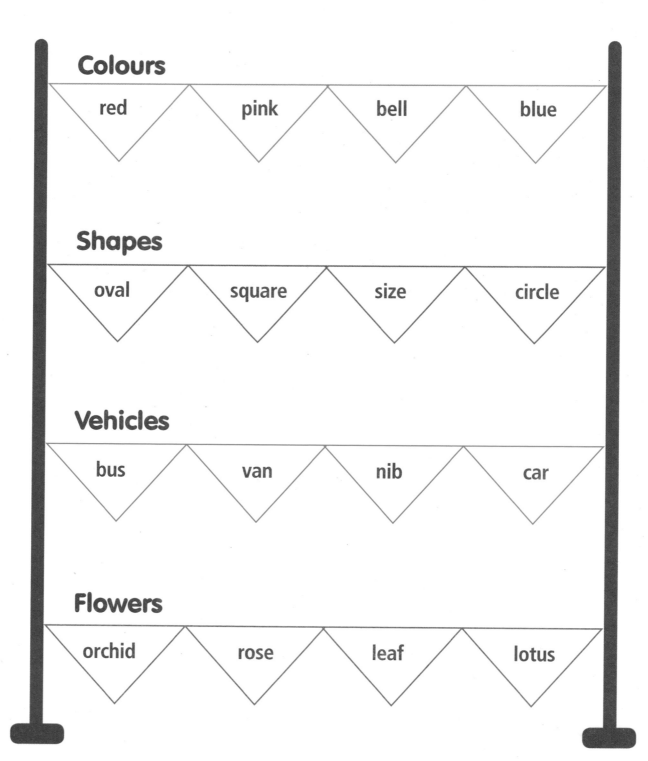

Make new words from the given letters and write in the space provided.

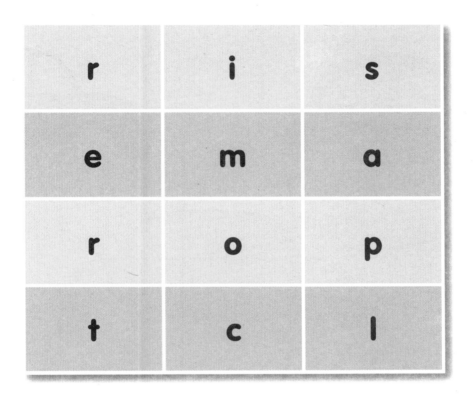

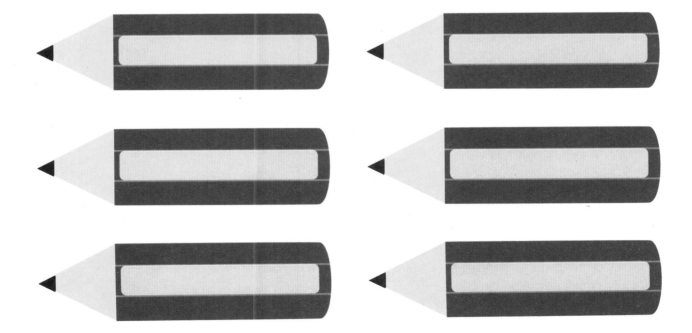

Join the words on tyres, which rhymes with the words written on the cars.